T3-BUV-208

VOLUME TWO

STAND OUT QUOTE JOURNAL™

Inspired By

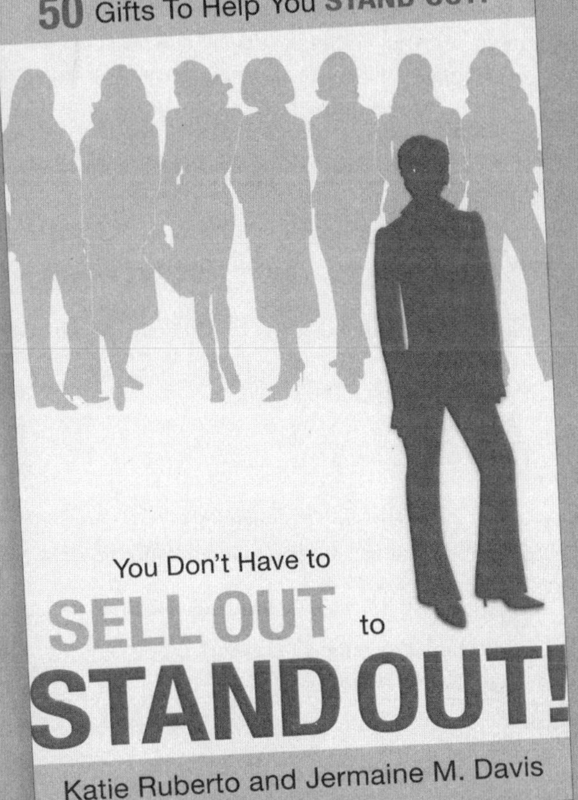
50 Gifts To Help You STAND OUT!
You Don't Have to
SELL OUT to
STAND OUT!
Katie Ruberto and Jermaine M. Davis

52 Quotes to Help You Succeed in Life, School & Work

Katie Ruberto and Jermaine M. Davis

ISBN 0-9673500-4-2

Library of Congress Cataloging-in-Publication Data has been filed for.

Manufactured and Printed in the United States of America

First Printing: Summer 2009

10 9 8 7 6 5 4 3 2 1

The Stand Out Leadership Company, LLC's books and audio products may be purchased in bulk for educational, business, fundraising or sales promotional use. For information please call (952) 594-5738.

The Stand Out Leadership Company, LLC
Katie Ruberto and Jermaine M. Davis
1259 Rose Vista Court
Roseville, MN 55113
Number (952) 594-5738
www.standoutleadership.com

Cover Design and Layout by Christina Lamski of Sunnyside Creative, LLC.
www.sunnysidecreative.com

Acknowledgements - Katie Ruberto

I have been blessed to have strong advocates in my life who have helped me become the woman I am today and continue to help me grow! I dedicate this book to the men who have believed in me and taught me "to play the game" and "Stand Out" while honoring my unique talents and strengths!

Jermaine M. Davis – Through your encouragement and support, I feel confident in my ability to lead and change lives; you have helped me find that inner passion and courage I needed to grow and succeed! Your stamp is all over this book... your insight is amazing! You inspire me...You make me a better person...Your ideas, your vision and your dedication is contagious! Your commitment to change, growth and development has helped to transform my life personally and professionally and many of those you come in contact with! I never get tired of watching you live out your TAGS; I am definitely one of your biggest fans! Jermaine, thank you so much for your support! You model what you teach and are a true testament to integrity. I cannot quantify my appreciation for all that you have given me...I am blessed to have you in my life!

Mike Gregoire – I am SO glad that I wandered onto your team. Sometimes I wonder where I would be if we never crossed paths. I credit my beginning professional growth to you; you taught me my first lessons about the workplace. You believed in me and stuck with me through all my challenges of adapting to the work environment and I can't thank you enough! You taught me how to use my strengths to my benefit; you taught me how to "play the game," to never sell out, but to STAND OUT in my own way! You opened the door for me to truly develop my strengths and to have the courage to leverage them! You are a model of GREAT leadership! No matter where I go in life, I will never forget you! Thank you so much!

Dr. Leo Ruberto – My father, you introduced me to my strength and courage! You always told me I could be anything I wanted and that I am meant for great things...you were right. I only wish that you were here to share with me my many accomplishments. Thank you for instilling in me belief in my abilities. Thank you for teaching me the value of education and studying! Thank you for laying the foundation for me to become a strong, successful woman! I miss you and love you very much!

Leo Ruberto, Jr. – The older I get, the more I know I need you in my life! You are becoming such a loving man and it is so great to get to know you on this level! You mean so very much to me and I find so much comfort having you around and talking with you! I love you, "Lee Lee" and I cannot wait to share in the next phase of our lives together! Thank you for being there and being such a great little brother!

Acknowledgements - Jermaine M. Davis

I was taught at age 13 to give honor unto whom honor is due. I believe no one and I mean no one succeeds in life, school or work without the help, guidance and assistance of others. **Quote Journal™ - Volume Two** is dedicated to ALL the females who inspired me and mentored me both formally or informally as I pursued my dreams, goals and aspirations.

Jane Foulser – Words cannot communicate or explain my admiration for you. You were my mother away from home when I attended Elmhurst College. Here are just a few adjectives that I think of when I think of you and how you influenced my life and career: Graceful, passionate, extremely caring and thoughtful, jovial, unique, empathetic and an AWESOME spiritual friend. Thank you for being the GREATEST college advisor and counselor ever.

Dr. Brenda Forester – I remember walking into your advanced sociology class (social problems) as a first year student. Although this was an advanced course for a first year student, you assured me that you would help me succeed in your class and ultimately you helped me succeed at Elmhurst College. You gave me a wonderful gift, Dr. Forester, and that is you believed in me and you communicated your belief in my ability to succeed and overcome adversity through your actions and with your words of regular encouragement. Well, you kept your promise and it extended beyond my four years at Elmhurst College. Thank you for being a student-centered college professor. You have inspired me to become a student-centered college professor as well.

Peggy Killian – Thank you for taking me under your wing and informally mentoring me while I was a lost young man trying to find my way in life at Elmhurst College. I recall us accidentally meeting in the Career Services Office and I remember you providing me with professional advice regarding internships, summer employment and employment after graduation. My spiritual beliefs teach me that there are no accidents in life Peggy, which means we were meant to meet and connect. I want to thank you and your husband for emotionally supporting me, listening to me and believing in me. I will never ever forget the many thought-provoking talks and discussions we shared.

Sharon Kemper – You gave me hope when I was 21 years young. I remember being that insecure teaching assistant at Duluth Community College (now Lake Superior College) who was afraid to teach Introduction to Public Speaking and Principles of Interpersonal Communication. I can still vividly picture the pep talks you gave me before each class until I developed the confidence to stand alone. Thank you for not giving up on me, and more importantly, for believing in me even when I doubted myself. You were the person who inspired me to teach at the community college level and guess what; I've been teaching at the community college level since November of 1997. Your inspiration led me to being nominated as College Instructor of the Year. Thank you for your inspiration!

Joyce Muse – Thank you for believing in me when I taught 5th and 6th grade to homeless youth in downtown Minneapolis. I remember when you used to tell me, "Jermaine you're a great teacher and educator because you have the ability to reach people in ways that most people cannot." I had many fears and apprehensions and I was filled with major self-doubt during those years and you were the kickstand that helped me to stand tall during those earlier years in my teaching career. I will never-ever forget ALL the heart-to-heart discussions we shared about life, love, work, spirituality and my plight in life as a young black man. Oh yeah, thank you for the Soul Food dinners you would bring to school and share with me from time to time (I needed those dinners back then because that was a period in my life when I was really-really hurting financially). Thank you Ms. Muse!

Dr. Sue Ehlers – Thank you for being a wonderful relationship-based leader as my dean at Century College. I can honestly say that I've experienced a leader in my professional career that I've been able to disagree with personally and professionally without fear of retaliation. Thank you for creating a healthy work environment where I feel I can be the best college professor in the world.

Thank you for checking in with me during my family crisis. I nominate you Dean of the Century!

Extra Special Appreciation

Katie Ruberto – I know I should thank you right now; however words are not enough to articulate my appreciation for ALL you bring to the significant work we do. I get so elated when you and I work on projects together because our chemistry has proven to be one of the best partnerships ever cultivated. Our polar opposites at times are the unique differences and added value we bring to our readers and supporters. Thank you for helping me become a better writer, co-author and business partner. Thank you for helping me expand my gender lens and detect many of my blind-spots in the area of women's issues and women's leadership. I feel so blessed, honored and fortunate to have you as a co-author and business partner. Hands down Katie you are the MOST talented person I've ever worked with in my life. Thank you for being in my life both, personally and professionally.

Please continue to share your TAGS (Talents, Abilities, Gifts and Skills) with the world because everyone should experience the **Katie Ruberto Effect**.

Carolyn "Charmaine" Davis - MOM I miss you! Guess what, MOM? WE DID IT AGAIN! I wish I could mail you an express copy of this latest project. You would be proud of this **Quote Journal**™. Thank you for your love and inspiration. You will never-ever be forgotten! Love your son,

Jermaine M. Davis a.k.a. J.D.

Introduction to YOUR QUOTE JOURNAL™

What is a Quote Journal™?

This is definitely not your typical quote book in which an author compiles a list of quotes from famous people to motivate and inspire readers. Rather, we have created a **Quote Journal**™ *to give you an opportunity to reflect and respond to thought-provoking questions prompted by a series of quotes.* Taken together, the quotes and questions will help you think about how best to improve your personal, professional and private life. We want our readers to begin each day motivated and inspired to achieve their dreams.

This **Quote Journal**'s™ ultimate goal is to help you become successful in life, school and work. Each quote invites you to reflect upon its meaning and relevance in your life. Reaping the full benefits of your **Quote Journal**™ requires that you reflect and respond to each question. As you read each quote, ask yourself, "How would the creator of this quote like me to apply this quote to my personal, professional and private life?" We want *you* to live a happier, healthier and more productive life! You can achieve this goal by determining what resonates with you and by exploring these quotes in a deep and meaningful way.

Why are Quotes a Source of Motivation and Inspiration?

Individuals are attracted to quotes for different reasons. Some people use quotes as refrigerator décor. Some people collect quotes to reinforce their central beliefs, values and priorities. Employees and students often place them at their workstations as sources of daily inspiration. Quotes allow us to look into the hearts, souls and minds of those we admire. Quotes allow us to experience a myriad of emotions. Quotes can make us think, laugh, cry, ponder, scream or yell. Quotes can motivate us to search for answers to our problems. Quotes are our "ten-second teachers" and can compel us to revolutionize our lives. You can learn valuable life lessons when you reflect upon and apply the women's words of wisdom in your **Quote Journal**.™

Great quotes derive from both women and men; however, our male-dominated society has valued (both consciously and unconsciously) men's words more highly than women's words. Throughout history and across cultures, women's words have been deemed unworthy of publicity. Women's experiences and perspectives have been devalued, dismissed and disregarded. These injustices still affect 21st century perceptions of women. Despite these perceptions, women throughout the ages have had much to say about life, love, education and the workplace; unfortunately, these ideas have not been publicized widely. Only in the last few decades or so has American society begun to take women's words of wisdom seriously. While we have great respect for both women's and men's life-changing and transformational quotes, we have deliberately chosen women's words to spotlight women's voices, experiences and perspectives. This **Quote Journal**™ pays special tribute to the courageous women who motivate, encourage and uplift *all* our readers!

What are "Stand Out" Quotes?

Within the context of this **Quote Journal**,™ "Stand Out" means to be noticed, acknowledged and recognized for one's positive contributions in life, school and work. We believe deeply that *all* human beings should be acknowledged and honored for their contributions to the world. We believe knowing *what* and *how* you contribute to the world is critical to cultivating high self-esteem.

"Stand Out" quotes compel us to give the quote undivided attention and reflection. The quotes we selected made a positive and powerful first impression on us. "Stand Out" quotes make us ponder where we are and where we desire to be in life, school and work. "Stand Out" quotes, if applied effectively to our personal, professional and private lives, can empower us to live the best lives possible.

You will inevitably "Stand Out" when you use your unique talents, abilities, gifts and skills (TAGS). Your TAGS include your innate and cultivated strengths. When you use your TAGS, you will automatically "Stand Out" in all you do in life, school and work. Journaling will prompt you to recall how your TAGS have allowed you to make a difference in others' lives. We want all of our **Quote Journal**™ readers to stand up, "Stand Out" and be honored and celebrated for their unique contributions.

What "Stand Out" Quotes are Not!

Standing out as an individual does not mean you bring unnecessary or undeserving attention to yourself. To "Stand Out" does not mean that you are an attention-starved, narcissistic egomaniac; there is nothing wrong with celebrating your achievements and accomplishments! What you write in your **Quote Journal**™ belongs to you and is written for your eyes only. We encourage you to be honest and forthright to maximize your journaling experience. Your **Quote Journal**™ does not replace professional counseling or therapy. However, you can refresh and renew your mind, body, soul and spirit by reflecting upon and writing responses to the questions posed in your **Quote Journal**™.

What Can Journaling Do For You?

Journaling does not have to be a dissertation-length interpretation of each quote. Instead, journaling allows you to record your spontaneous and authentic thoughts as you liberate your mind and emotions. Journaling is a form of *intra*personal communication; journaling allows you to communicate with yourself authentically. Journaling can help you heal and overcome hurt. Journaling can help you recover your fun, joy and laughter lost in life's stormy moments.

Please journal by addressing the questions posed after each quote. You may also journal "freehand" by describing your thoughts, feelings and aspirations as they relate to the quoted material. Explore each quote's meaning as *you* interpret them. Remember: the ultimate goal of journaling is to help you live a happier, healthier and more productive life.

We all learn in different ways and require different tools and resources to achieve our personal and professional dreams, so it is important to think about how journaling can assist you on your journey toward success. Journaling can facilitate self-discovery, self-reflection, soul development and personal transformation. Journaling can:

- Ignite hidden and untapped passion. Allow yourself to feel the women's energy behind the quotes inside your **Quote Journal**.™

- Increase personal and professional effectiveness. Quotes can motivate you to realize your grandest dreams and goals.

- Evoke emotions that have been hidden and tucked away. Journaling can help you release toxic emotions; in just a few words, quotes can tug at your heart and arouse emotions you had not thought about in a long time.

- Stimulate creative and innovative thinking. Writing in your **Quote Journal**™ can inspire your curiosity, which is a valuable asset and competitive advantage in today's marketplace.

- Solidify your beliefs in the midst of ambiguity and uncertainty. Journaling tends to clarify your beliefs and values. The quotes invite and challenge you to examine your thoughts, beliefs and values more deeply.

- Destroy fallacies and misconceptions you may hold about yourself and others. Journaling can help you differentiate between subjective and objective thinking; journaling can also balance your thoughts between the ideal and real world.

- Improve personal and professional focus. You may not know where you are going or what is important to you. Journaling will help you develop a laser-beam focus and vision to direct your personal and professional path.

Of course, journaling can provide other positive benefits. We understand that journaling is a private activity and we encourage you to take the process to a level you find most comfortable. It is fine to journal for a short time and revisit your journal from time to time. We know that journaling can transform *your* life. We look forward to *you* living *your* best life!

How Should You Use Your **Quote Journal**™?

We encourage you to write extensively in your new **Quote Journal**.™ The 100+ questions inside your **Quote Journal**™ will challenge you to "dig deep" inside your soul to discover the best answers to help you succeed in life, love, school and work.

Before you begin writing, please select your favorite writing instrument and a special setting: a living-room nook, a coffee shop or a place that has special meaning for you as you embark upon this revolutionary and life-transforming activity. We ask that you invest a minimum of 15, 20 or 30 minutes per day to read, reflect and write in your **Quote Journal**.™ You will grow exponentially as you reflect on the quotes and as you record your responses. You *must* be willing to answer *all* of the **Quote Journal**'s™ questions in order to cultivate the personal and professional life you desire. Remember: success requires dedication, determination and discipline.

Your **Quote Journal**™ should be something you read and reflect upon continuously and regularly. Looking back on the thoughts and emotions you expressed in your **Quote Journal**™ allows you to ask yourself:

- "Did I achieve my objectives?"
- "Am I accomplishing the goals I wrote about?"
- "Am I living my values and a purpose-driven life?"

You will eventually find new ideas to add to your **Quote Journal**™ because you are constantly evolving as a human being. Face it: you will have put too much *quality* and *quantity* time into your **Quote Journal**™ to abandon it on a bookshelf as soon as you complete it!

We believe in *your* ability to succeed and achieve greatness, and we wish you the best success in all you do! Please allow the words of these wise and talented women to help you create the best life possible!

YOUR QUOTE JOURNAL™

QUOTE #1 Maya Angelou

"Someone was hurt before you; wronged before you; hungry before you; frightened before you; beaten before you; humiliated before you; raped before you; yet, someone survived."

We all experience unfortunate situations. What unfortunate situations have you experienced? How do you plan to move forward?

How will moving past your unfortunate experiences alleviate pain and stress in your life?

QUOTE #2 **Gwendolyn Brooks**

"What makes you think the world owes you something?"

Some people struggle with issues of entitlement. Do you think the world owes you something? If so, what do you think the world owes you?

I feel like the world owes me a space where I can be comfortable - not always conscious of my unique set of cultures - but okay reppin' all of them. I think this is an internal feeling - I think I have these spaces but have trouble recognizing them & being comfortable in them because I have trouble being comfortable in my own skin.

Describe someone you know who believes the world owes them something. How has this belief shaped their communication style?

QUOTE #3 — Coco Chanel

"How many cares one loses when one decides not to be something, but to be someone."

What is the difference between being *something* verses *someone*? Explain.

How do you become *someone*? Provide examples.

QUOTE #4 — Anne Frank

"The final forming of a person's character lies in their own hands."

Define the word character. What individuals contributed to the formation of your character? What are you doing to make sure you are shaping the character you want to represent you?

Anne Frank suffered greatly in her short lifetime, but she formed a powerful character. How would your family members, friends and colleagues describe your character?

QUOTE #5 — Eva Le Gallienne

"Innovators are inevitably controversial."

Are there times in your life where you have held back on being the innovator because you didn't want to stand out? Explain. Do you work in an innovative-friendly environment?

What would it take for your innovative side to live curiously and blissfully? Describe the benefits of innovation.

QUOTE #6 Sophia Loren

"Mistakes are a part of the dues one pays for a full life."

Do you "play it safe" or do you "take risks?" Explain. How do you feel after you make a mistake? How can making mistakes advance your professional career?

Do you share your mistakes with others? Why or why not? How can sharing your mistakes help others succeed in life, school & work?

QUOTE #7 Mother Teresa

"Kind words can be short and easy to speak, but their echoes are truly endless."

If kind words are so easy to speak, then why don't people use them more often? Explain.

Provide an example of a time when you were acknowledged and complimented. How did this make you feel?

QUOTE #8 Sylvia Robinson

"The glass ceiling doesn't apply when you're building your own house."

Have women transcended the glass ceiling by starting their own businesses? Why or why not?

Identify other options you could explore to transcend or to break the glass ceiling. Explain.

QUOTE #9 Deborah Tannen

"We all know we are unique individuals, but we tend to see others as representatives of groups."

Describe the personal and professional danger of seeing an individual as a member of a group rather than as an unique individual. What prevents us from seeing people as individuals?

Describe a time in your life when you were stereotyped and put in a particular group when *you* wanted to be seen as an individual. Describe how that experience made you feel.

QUOTE #10 Harriet Tubman

"I never ran my train off the track, and I never lost a passenger."

What do you think Harriet Tubman was trying to communicate? What characteristics does it take to embark on a large project without making ***ANY*** grave mistakes?

Why would Harriet Tubman risk her freedom and life so many times when she was already safe? Would you do what Harriet Tubman did? Why or why not?

QUOTE #11 Oprah Winfrey

"I was once afraid of people saying, 'Who does she think she is?' Now I have the courage to stand and say, 'This is who I am'."

Do you have the self-confidence to say what Oprah said? Why or why not? Why do you believe Oprah was once fearful of other people's perception of her?

Who are you NOW in life? Explain. Are *you* comfortable being *you*? Explain.

Olga Knopf

"The art of being a woman can never consist of being a bad imitation of a man."

In order to advance in male-dominated work environments, is it necessary for women to act like men? Explain.

Historically, some women acted like men to achieve acceptance and success. What were the costs of those actions?

QUOTE #13 — Helen Keller

"Security is mostly a superstition. It does not exist in nature. Life is either a daring adventure or nothing."

Do you see your life as a daring adventure, or do you operate under the illusion of security? Describe a time when you lived life as a daring adventure.

What prevents people from living adventurous lives? Please explain.

QUOTE #14 — Joan Baez

"You don't get to choose how you're going to die. Or when. You can only decide how you're going to live. Now."

Provide two examples of how you have taken advantage of life's opportunities. What benefits did you gain from these experiences? Explain.

How would you teach the meaning of this quote to an 18-year-old starting her life's journey?

QUOTE #15 Mary H. Waldrip

"It's important that people should know what you stand for. It's equally important that they know what you won't stand for."

Do your family members, friends and colleagues know what you stand for? What have you done to communicate and demonstrate your position or perspective? Explain.

Do your family members, friends and colleagues know what you *do not* stand for? What have you done to communicate and demonstrate your position or perspective? Explain.

QUOTE #16 Rita Mae Brown

"Good judgment comes from experience, and often experience comes from bad judgment."

Describe a time when you used good judgment. What lessons did you learn from this experience? Explain.

Describe a time when you used bad judgment. What lessons did you learn from this experience? Explain.

QUOTE #17 Barbara Grizzuti-Harrison

"All acts performed in the world begin in the imagination."

Describe three acts that began in your imagination.

What ideas have you imagined but have not yet enacted? What prevented you from acting on these ideas? Please be descriptive.

Pam Shaw

"If you take too long in deciding what to do with your life, you'll find you've done it."

One of the most pondered questions today is, "What should I do with my life?" What are your personal and professional goals in life, school & work?

Are you doing what you thought you would be doing? Why or why not?

QUOTE #19 Amelia Earhart

"I want to do it because I want to do it. Women must try to do things as men have tried. If they fail, their failure must be but a challenge for others."

Do you allow others' failures to define you? Do others' failures inspire you to keep challenging yourself? Explain your position.

Name a time when you took on a challenge. What does the phrase "fail forward" mean to you?

Susan B. Anthony

"Independence is happiness."

Historically, American women were socialized to depend on men. Presently, many women have adopted a new paradigm of independence as they fight to eradicate sexism and gender inequities and inequalities. Explain how independence can lead to happiness.

Explain why it is ***so*** important for younger women to understand and embrace independence. Explain how independence has led to happiness in ***your*** life.

QUOTE #21 Evita Peron

"You must want! You have the right to ask! You must desire."

Describe a time when you wanted to achieve a specific goal so badly that you couldn't relax until you took action. What proactive skills did you learn that you can apply to all areas of your life?

What do you think Evita Peron meant when she stated, "You have the right to ask?"

QUOTE #22 Eleanor Roosevelt

"It is not fair to ask of others what you are not willing to do yourself."

Sometimes we must do things we would rather not in order to contribute to the team's or relationship's goals. Describe a time when you had to do something that you really didn't want to do, but it supported the needs of the team or the relationship.

Have you ever had to ask someone to do something they didn't want to do, but it was important to the team or the relationship? How did the conversation go? How did you encourage their participation?

QUOTE #23 Lois Wyse

"Men are taught to apologize for their weaknesses, women for their strengths."

Describe a time when you apologized unnecessarily. Where and from whom did you learn to apologize? Do you agree that women and men are socialized to apologize differently? Why or why not?

Do you think women are "labeled" when they demonstrate their strengths? If so, what labels are used to describe strong women? How can demonstrating your strengths help or hinder others' perceptions of you?

QUOTE #24 Ruby Dee

"The greatest gift is not being afraid to question."

Do you have the courage to ask questions? Have you avoided asking questions for the fear that people might think your questions are silly or stupid? Provide examples.

Why do you think Ruby Dee described the courage to question as "the greatest gift?" Explain.

QUOTE #25 Christiane Collage

"When you belong to a minority, you have to be better in order to have the right to be equal."

Describe a time when you had to work harder than most people to get ahead in life, school & work. Elaborate in detail.

Do you agree with Christiane Collage's statement? Explain why or why not.

QUOTE #26 — Pearl Bailey

"No one can figure out your worth but you."

How much are you worth intellectually, emotionally and spiritually? Explain. How can you discern your worth in life, school & work?

How much value do you provide to others (not financially)? What is your relationship value? Friendship value? Workplace value? Explain.

QUOTE #27 **Billie Holiday**

"I'm ready to close this chapter of my life."

Billie Holiday implies that we all reach turning points in our lives. Name the relationships, situations or jobs that are chapters in your life that you're ready to close once and for all.

- safely making money
- being fully dependent on salary
- no passive income
- waiting for marriage to enjoy this stage
- waiting for partner for baby #2
- feeling inadequate / hiding my light
  - not loving my light

Explain a time when you or someone you know closed a chapter in their life. Describe the specific challenges that you or the other person faced when the chapter was closed.

#1 goal: 815 credit score
#2 goal: Real estate lisense
#3 goal: finish basement (2nd income)

QUOTE #28 Minna Antrim

"Experience is a good teacher but she runs up big bills."

Minna Antrim discusses how some lessons are harder to learn than others. Think back to a time when you learned a tough lesson through experience. Was it worth it? Why or why not?

In what other ways can you learn lessons and save time and money?

QUOTE #29 Mary Kay Ash

"I find that if you must criticize, it is best to sandwich it between two layers of praise."

Mary Kay Ash believes that negative critiques should contain positive messages as well. Do you agree or disagree? Explain.

How can you deliver unfavorable news without harming a person's self-esteem and/or self-concept? Is it possible to do so? Please explain.

QUOTE #30 Marva Collins

"Success doesn't come to you. You go to it."

Name someone you know who believes success will come to them. Name someone you know who goes after success.

How does *hard work* differ from *luck*?

QUOTE #31 **Princess Diana**

"When you are happy you can forgive a great deal."

Do you agree with Princess Diana's quote? Why or why not?

Do you believe it is difficult to forgive when you are unhappy? Explain. When was the last time you told someone you were sorry? How difficult was it for you to apologize? Explain.

QUOTE #32 **Nikki Giovanni**

***"If you don't understand yourself,
you don't understand anybody else."***

What are the most effective ways to learn about yourself and others?

Failing to understand others can cause problems at home, school & work. When has not understanding someone led to conflict or interpersonal problems in your life?

QUOTE #33 **Oprah Winfrey**

"Don't depend on forces outside of yourself to get ahead."

Why do you think Oprah Winfrey discourages depending on outside forces to get ahead in life, school & work?

How does depending on outside forces prevent you from getting ahead? Explain.

QUOTE #34 Wilma Rudolph

"No matter what great things you may accomplish in life, somebody helps you."

Name the individuals who have helped you on your life's journey thus far. Explain how each person has contributed to your life in their unique way.

How have you or how will you "pay back" the individuals who have helped you achieve success?

QUOTE #35 Lily Tomlin

"For fast-acting relief try slowing down."

Define and distinguish between "stress" and "burnout." What does it mean to "slow down?" How often do you slow down? Explain.

How do your mind, body and emotions communicate with you when you need to slow down? Please provide examples.

QUOTE #36 Michelle Ventour

"Potential means you ain't doing nothing now."

Name three people you know who have potential but fail to act on it. In your opinion, what seems to prevent them from maximizing their full potential?

Explain the phrase, "She or he has great potential." If you are in a relationship and you love that person, how long should you wait for that individual's potential to manifest? Please explain.

QUOTE #37 Rose Zadra (age 6)

"If you love someone, then hurry up and show it."

How do you intentionally show love to the people you love or care about? Why do some people hold back their love when they feel it? Can you miss out on an opportunity to love someone? Explain.

What do you think 6-year-old Rose Zadra saw in her life to motivate her to make such a powerful and empathic statement? Explain.

QUOTE #38 Jennifer Granholm

"I urge you to be bold. Life isn't changed from the balcony. Get onto the floor and dance, dance, dance."

To what extent do you observe life rather than living it?

How would your life and career change if you took Jennifer Granholm's advice?

QUOTE #39 **Toni Morrison**

"If you're going to hold someone down you're going to have to hold on by the other end of the chain. You are confined by your own repression."

What did Toni Morrison mean by the statement, "You are confined by your own repression?" Please explain.

Provide an example of a time when you witnessed someone holding someone else down. How did you respond? What was it like to witness that situation?

QUOTE #40 Beverly Sills

"You may be disappointed if you fail, but you are doomed if you don't try."

What is the difference between disappointment and doom? Would you rather feel disappointed or doomed? Explain.

Describe a time when you were disappointed because you did not achieve a goal. What steps did you take to overcome your disappointment?

QUOTE #41 Pearl S. Buck

"Every great mistake has a halfway moment, a split second when it can be recalled and perhaps remedied."

Identify three skills necessary for being able to "see" the "halfway moments."

What prevents people from catching mistakes early on?

QUOTE #42 Margaret Thatcher

"You cannot lead from the crowd."

Distinguish between a leader who leads from the crowd and a leader who leads from outside the crowd. What are the advantages and disadvantages of both approaches to leadership?

Do you prefer to lead within the crowd or outside the crowd? Explain.

QUOTE #43 — Arlene Raven

"The way in which we think of ourselves has everything to do with how our world sees us."

How do your self-perceptions affect how others see and treat you? Are you happy with how others see and treat you personally and professionally? Explain.

How would a biographer describe you to the world?

QUOTE #44 Amy Alcott

"Don't give advice unless you're asked."

Unwanted and unsolicited advice can be perceived as judgmental. Name a time when someone gave you unwanted and unsolicited advice. How did you react?

Describe a time when you gave unwanted and unsolicited advice to someone. What did you learn from this interaction? Please explain.

QUOTE #45 Harriet Beecher Stowe

"When you get into a tight place and everything goes against you, till it seems as though you could not hang on a minute longer, never give up then, for that is just the place and time that the tide will turn."

Describe a time in your life when you thought you could "not hang on a minute longer." Explain how the tide turned at this difficult moment in life.

How can you tell when the "tide" is turning in your favor? Explain.

QUOTE #46 Sandra Day O'Connor

"Each of us brings to our job, whatever it is, our lifetime of experiences and our values."

We all bring unique experiences, values and perspectives to our teams. Name the most important experiences, values and perspectives you bring to your team.

Choose two people on your team and journal about what you have learned from each person's experiences, values and perspectives.

QUOTE #47 Jane Goodall

"Lasting change is a series of compromises. And compromise is all right, as long as your values don't change."

Describe a time when you were asked to compromise and the request conflicted with your values. Did you honor the request to compromise? Why or why not?

Is it possible to compromise and yet maintain your values? Explain your answer and provide an example.

QUOTE #48 Ellen Parr

"The cure for boredom is curiosity. There is no cure for curiosity."

Define "boredom" and "curiosity" in your own words. Explain how curiosity cures boredom.

Describe three things you can do to spark your own or others' curiosity. Describe three things you can do to overcome boredom.

QUOTE #49 **Lorraine Hansberry**

"A woman who is willing to be herself and pursue her own potential runs not so much the risk of loneliness as the challenge of exposure to more interesting men – and people in general."

Why are people drawn to women who are willing to be themselves? Why is this attribute so appealing?

Why might some people believe that a woman's willingness to be herself might cause loneliness? Do you believe that being yourself will cause you to be lonely? Why or why not?

QUOTE #50 Marie Curie

"Nothing in life is to be feared. It is only to be understood."

What deliberate steps are you taking to understand the fears that are blocking your success in life, school & work?

What is the difference between the fear of failure, the fear of rejection and the fear of success?

QUOTE #51 **Janie Mines**

"Don't be afraid to go out on a limb. That's where the fruit is."

Describe a time when you took a deliberate risk. What fears did you have about taking that risk? Explain how you were able to overcome your fear.

Make a list of the pros and cons of taking risks in life, school & work.

QUOTE #52 **Bette Reese**

"If you think you are too small to be effective, you've never been in bed with a mosquito."

What do Bette Reese's words mean to you?

Describe a time when you felt too small to be effective. How did you overcome this feeling?

CLOSING THOUGHTS

Closing Thoughts, Ideas and Next Steps

Now that you have finished reading, reflecting upon and recording answers to the prompts in your **Quote Journal**,™ what steps should you take next? What will you do with those insightful, wonderful journal entries? Did you labor in vain? As co-authors of your **Quote Journal**,™ Katie and Jermaine would like you to continue your journey by considering the following questions:

- What does your **Quote Journal**™ reveal to you about your values, beliefs, priorities and feelings?
- What "next steps" can you take to fulfill your dreams in life, school and work?
- What decisions have you reached?
- What future decisions will you need to make to improve your life?
- What insights have you gained about yourself, your family, your co-workers, your spouse or your significant other?
- Which friends will you keep? Which friends will you need to let go?
- Which relationships will you need to redefine and renegotiate?
- Did you discover what you want to be when you grow up?
- What are your career ambitions and aspirations?
- What kind of business will you start? What kind of franchise will you own and operate?
- Which mentors have you identified to help you reach the next level?
- Did you discover your **TAGS** (Talents, Abilities, Gifts and Skills)?
- Did you discover what it means to love, to be loved and to be *in* love?
- Do you *now* know why you wear your heart on your sleeve?

- Did you discover why you might be detached emotionally in your relationships?
- What did you learn about your religious and spiritual beliefs?
- Did you learn how to forgive? Can you now distinguish between forgiving and forgetting? Did you discover how grudges can debilitate and destroy your mental, emotional, physical and spiritual well-being?

Our hearts' desire is for you to live a happy, healthy and hopeful life marked by success and prosperity. We want your journaling experiences to enrich you mentally, emotionally and spirituality. We ask that you *never* depart from your **Quote Journal**.™ We ask that you take momentary breaks from journaling to learn, ***un***learn and ***re***learn significant lessons about life, love, school and work. As you do so, please record these new insights inside your **Quote Journal**.™

The Marriage: The Commitment between You and Your **Quote Journal**™

The **Quote Journal**'s™ introduction asked you to journal introspectively *every*day. Journaling allows you to *see* your thoughts and emotions clearly, and then you can develop a clear vision for the life you seek ultimately to create.

We encourage you to journal for a minimum of 15, 20 or 30 minutes per day. Yes—we know you are busy! Yes—we understand you have multiple, competing priorities! This is why we have provided you with a range of journaling options! You may be asking yourself, "Can I *really* change my life by writing for 15, 20 or 30 minutes a day?" The answer is an astounding YES!

Ask yourself, "Can **91** hours, **121** hours or **182** hours help me create the life I desire?" We know you cannot change your life in one day or overnight. We also know that significant transformation takes time. We know from personal experience one's life can transform if one journals thoughtfully and intentionally for **91**, **121** or **182** hours per year. Study the following equations:

What does 15 minutes of journaling per day equal in one year?
15 minutes a day x 7 days a week =**105** minutes of ***weekly*** journal time
105 minutes of weekly journal time x 52 weeks in a year = **5,480** minutes of ***annual*** journal time
5,480 minutes of journal time ***divided by*** 60 minutes per hour = **91 Hours of Annual Journal Time!**

What does 20 minutes of journaling per day equal in one year?
20 minutes a day x 7 days a week =**140** minutes of ***weekly*** journal time
140 minutes of weekly journal time x 52 weeks in a year = **7,280** minutes of ***annual*** journal time
7,280 minutes of journal time ***divided by*** 60 minutes per hour = **121 Hours of Annual Journal Time!**

What does 30 minutes of journaling per day equal in one year?
30 minutes a day x 7 days a week =**210** minutes of ***weekly*** journal time
210 minutes of weekly journal time x 52 weeks in a year = **10,920** minutes of ***annual*** journal time
10,920 minutes of journal time ***divided by*** 60 minutes per hour = **182 Hours of Annual Journal Time!**

Katie and Jermaine wish you great success on your quest to live your ***best*** life. Please e-mail us and let us know how you have transformed your life by writing and journaling in your **Quote Journal**!™

Thank You For Journaling Toward Your Success!™

Other Products by The Stand Out Leadership Company

Quote Journal™ Series

The **Quote Journal™ Series** was created to help individuals achieve maximum happiness, peace and success in life, school and work. **Quote Journals™** provide readers and journalers with an opportunity to reflect and respond to thought-provoking questions prompted by a series of quotes. The quotes and questions will help each person think about how to best improve their personal and professional life. We want each reader and journaler to begin each day motivated and inspired to pursue their dreams.

Quote Journal™ Audio Series

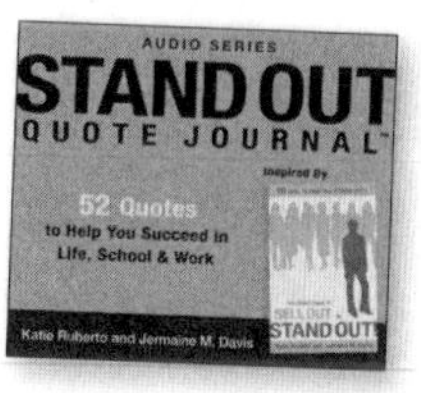

The **Quote Journal™ Audio Book Series** was created to give readers and journalers a small break from writing. We have created an audio book for each of the four **Quote Journals™** which allows readers and journalers to learn and listen through a different communication medium. We encourage each person to listen to their audio books while driving, cleaning, running, working out or while they are meditating and relaxing. The **Quote Journal™ Audio Book Series** is an excellent way to start or end a day as you live a life full of meaning and purpose.

You Don't Have to Sell Out to Stand Out! (50 Gifts To Help You STAND OUT)

This book was written to provide women with specific tips and strategies to help them successfully STAND OUT in life, school and work! This book is based on the experiences and insights taken from the hundreds of women we interviewed from across the country. The wisdom that we gleamed from these women's experiences and insights are called Stand Out Gifts. The 50 Stand Out Gifts inside ***You Don't Have to Sell Out to Stand Out*** will help women STAND OUT successfully in all areas of their lives.

Leading with Greatness and Be Diversity Competent

Leading with Greatness was written for anyone who desires to learn the foundations of effective leadership. Topics include: establishing credibility, building trust, motivating others and effectively resolving team conflict. ***Be Diversity Competent*** was written to teach individuals how to communicate appropriately, confidently and effectively with diverse people. This book provides readers with over 15 practical skills and tips to use during diverse encounters and interactions.

Get Up Off Your Butt & Do It NOW, The NOW Factors of College Success and Lessons from the Road

Get Up Off Your Butt & Do It NOW incorporates Jermaine's core motivational and inspirational principles for maintaining and sustaining personal and professional motivation. ***The NOW Factors of College Success*** was written specifically to help high school and college students achieve educational and academic success. ***Lessons from the Road*** was written with a few of Jermaine's professional colleagues and friends. Each writer shares her or his time tested principles for successful living!

If you would like to bring Katie Ruberto or Jermaine M. Davis to your organization or school for a presentation, weekend retreat or book signing; please contact our corporate office at:

Phone: (952) 594-5738

E-Mail: katie@standoutleadership.com or jermaine@jermainedavis.com

Website: www.standoutleadership.com

About The Author: Katie Ruberto

Katie Ruberto is Co-Founder and President of **The Stand Out Leadership Company**, an organization that specializes in developing leadership workshops and retreats as well as creating learning resources and products to help individuals grow and develop, both personally and professionally. Katie spent approximately ten years in Corporate America serving in many managerial and leadership roles as Project Manager, Marketing and Communications Lead and Diversity and Inclusion Manager within Human Resources. She is currently a Faculty Member at the University of Phoenix where she teaches Cultural Diversity. Katie is co-author of 5 books and 5 audio books including: *The Stand Out Quote Journal™ Series* and the groundbreaking book, *You Don't Have to Sell Out to Stand Out!*

Katie loves to travel! As a teenager and young adult she spent time traveling globally to countries and communities including Saudi Arabia, Europe, Asia and Africa. Katie attended and graduated from The American School in Switzerland located in Lugano, Switzerland. She earned a BA in International Studies with a concentration in Middle Eastern Studies from American University in Washington, DC. Katie holds an MBA in Marketing and she was recently recognized as a Cornell Certified Diversity Professional (CCDP) through its Diversity Management Program (a designation held for less than 300 individuals in the country). Katie is currently pursuing a Doctorate of Education in Organizational Leadership with focuses in the areas of Women's Leadership and Diversity Leadership.

Katie truly believes in community service and giving back to others. You can find Katie on any given weekday or Saturday volunteering for Last Hope (an organization committed to fostering and finding homes for abused and neglected animals). She is an active Board Member for the MultiCultural Development Center (MCDC) and a volunteer for Hope for Tomorrow (an organization dedicated to empowering young women and creating confident future female leaders). Currently, Katie resides in Eagan, MN with her dog Devon.

About the Author: Jermaine M. Davis

Jermaine M. Davis is an award winning Professor of Communication Studies at Century College in Minnesota. He has been teaching college adults to communicate effectively for the past twelve years; during his tenure Jermaine received the prestigious student-nominated College Instructor of the Year Award. Jermaine holds a MA in Speech Communication and a second MA in Education with a concentration in Teaching and Learning. Cornell University recently recognized Jermaine as a Cornell Certified Diversity Professional (CCDP) through its Diversity Management Program (a designation held for less than 300 people in the Country). He is currently pursuing a Doctorate of Education in Organizational Leadership with concentrations in the areas of Women's Leadership, Courageous Leadership and Diversity Leadership.

Jermaine grew up in the Henry Horner's housing projects on the west-side of Chicago in a single-parent home with three siblings. After losing six family members to violent deaths, Jermaine enrolled in college and began studying success and motivational principles to change the direction of his life. Now, he is the author and co-author of 10 books and 5 audio books including: Get *Up Off Your Butt & Do It NOW*, *Leading with Greatness*, *Be Diversity Competent*, *Lessons from the Road*, *The NOW Factors of College Success*, *You Don't Have to Sell Out to Stand Out* and *The Stand Out Quote Journal™ Series.*

Jermaine is the CEO, Co-Founder and President of two companies: Seminars & Workshops, Inc. and The Stand Out Leadership Company, both organizations specialize in providing workshops and creating learning resources and products to help individuals grow and develop personally and professionally in life, school and work. He is recognized as one of the country's most requested keynote speakers, workshop leaders and college entertainers. Jermaine delivers keynotes and workshops to some of America's leading organizations including 3M, Best Buy, Wells Fargo, American Express, Enterprise Rent-A-Car and the United Way. Jermaine is a native of Chicago, IL and now resides in St. Paul, MN.

Most importantly, Jermaine still loves to eat his grandmother's homemade macaroni and cheese!